D1203444

DEDICATIONS

The author wishes to dedicate this book to my grandchildren Zara and Cooper,
who bring me more joy than they can ever know.
Also, a very special thank you to my husband Victor,
who has always supported me with love and wisdom in my varied ventures.

The illustrator wishes to dedicate this book to her two inspirational children, Blaine and Aubrey,
and to her supportive and loving husband, Hector.

The author and illustrator want to thank our dear friend Shelly Strauss,
who brought us together to begin this beautiful journey into the publishing world of children's concept books.

Library of Congress Cataloging-in-Publication Data
Printed in China through Four Colour Print Group
Production Date: 02/17/11
Plant & Location: Printed by Everbest Printing Co. Guangdong, China
Job/Batch#: 98118
ISBN 978-0-615-40121-8
1.Bedtime made peaceful 2.Parenting 3. Life Concepts & Skills for children 4.Teaching life concepts

PEACEFULLY COLORFULLY BEAUTIFULLY BEDTIME

Written by Darlene Liss
Illustrated by Tabitha Blaine

Some people like to count
white fluffy sheep.
Some people like to read a book
to help them fall asleep.

Some people like to drink
a cup of nice warm milk.
Others like to wrap themselves
in soft, smooth silk.

So put on your favorite pj's
and say all your "goodnights."
Snuggle under the covers deep,
and turn down all the lights.

With your eyes closed very tightly
start to REALLY concentrate.

You can do this magic nightly,
and it always turns out great!

Try to imagine
the colors of the Rainbow
one by one.
RED
BLUE

Now you can start to have some fun.

When you want to see RED, concentrate hard
and picture the roses in the next yard.
Of course a RED fire truck would do just as well
or a shiny RED apple would be perfectly swell.

A big round ORANGE comes next
delicious and sweet,
a glass of OJ or a lollipop treat.

a bright ORANGE sunset
that lights up the sky,
or ORANGE cones in the street
which tell you not to go by.

Picture YELLOW in your mind, the color of the SU

r your shiny YELLOW slicker when it's raining as you run.

See the flames of your birthday candles
as you make your special wishes,
or the YELLOW rubber gloves
when your dad is washing dishes.

GREEN is the color
of all kinds of trees,
the leaves of flowers
and the grass under your feet.
Living "GREEN" means the Earth
needs our tender loving care.
You have an important part to play
by doing your share!

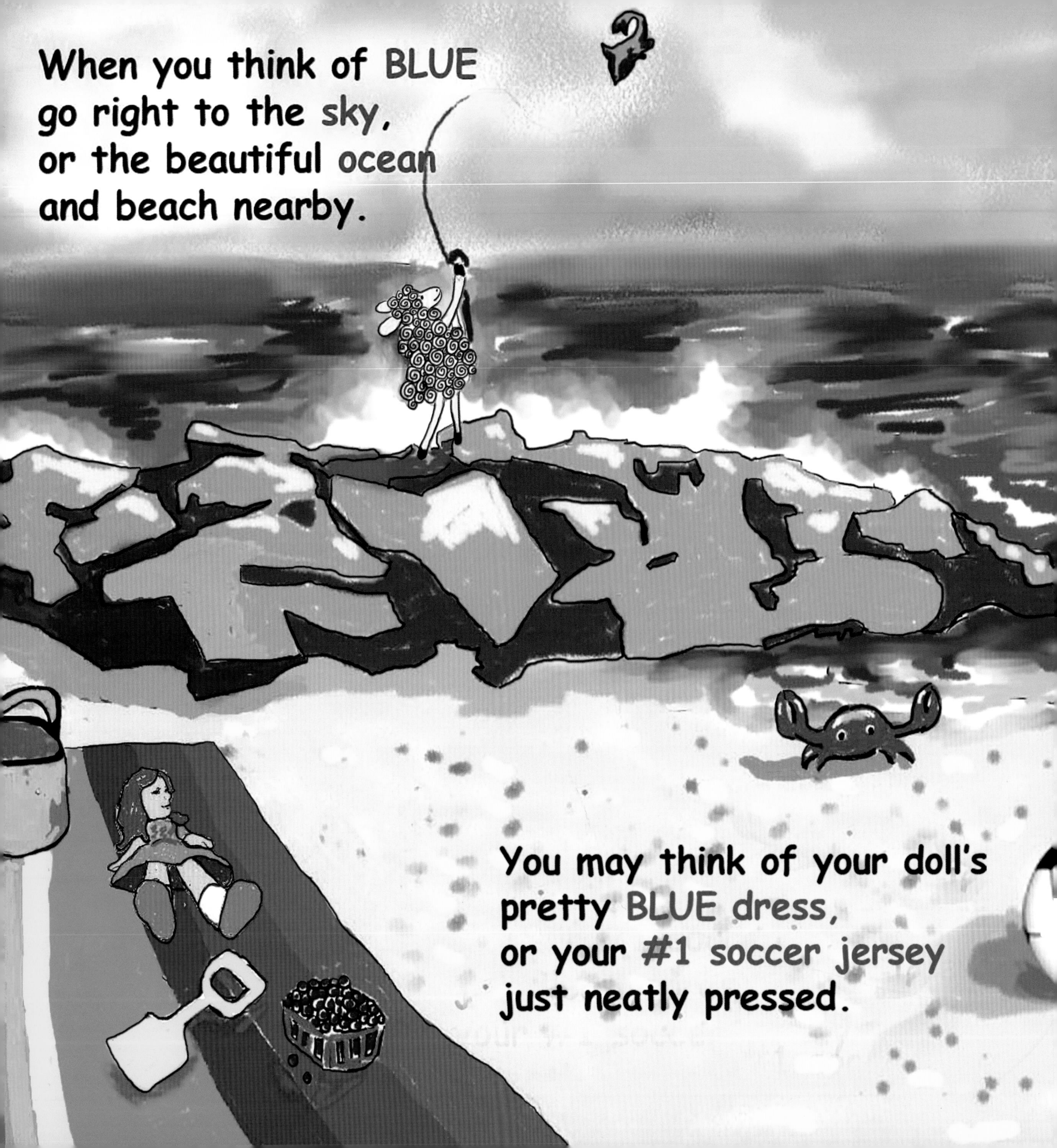

When you think of BLUE
go right to the sky,
or the beautiful ocean
and beach nearby.

You may think of your doll's
pretty BLUE dress,
or your #1 soccer jersey
just neatly pressed.

INDIGO is like purple, the grape juice you drink,
or the marker you use, the one with purple ink.
You can picture an eggplant, but that's pretty hard,
or the purple on your playhouse in your own backyard.

The last color of the rainbow is VIOLET,
but you're not asleep just yet.
Think lilacs and ribbons and soft cotton candy.
That should put you to sleep, just fine and dandy!

So try this yourself
when you go to sleep at night.
Concentrate hard and close your eyes tight.
Picture the colors of the Rainbow
in your head,
and you will have
FUN

GOING TO BED!